W9-BSS-844

Cool Dog, School Dog

Story by
Deborah Heiligman

illustrated by
Tim Bowers

SCHOLASTIC INC.
New York Toronto London Auckland
Sydney Mexico City New Delhi Hong Kong

No part of this publication may be reproduced, stored in a retrieval system,
or transmitted in any form or by any means, electronic, mechanical, photocopying,
recording, or otherwise, without written permission of the publisher. For information
regarding permission, write to Marshall Cavendish Corporation,
99 White Plains Road, Tarrytown, NY 10591.

ISBN 978-0-545-27306-0

Text copyright © 2009 by Deborah Heiligman.
Illustrations copyright © 2009 by Tim Bowers. All rights reserved.
Published by Scholastic Inc., 557 Broadway, New York, NY 10012,
by arrangement with Marshall Cavendish Corporation, c/o The Chudney Agency.
SCHOLASTIC and associated logos are trademarks and/or registered trademarks of Scholastic Inc.

12 11 10 9 8 7 6 5 4 3 2 1   10 11 12 13 14 15/0

Printed in the U.S.A.   40

First Scholastic printing, September 2010

The illustrations are rendered in acrylic paint on three-ply bristol board.
Editor: Margery Cuyler
Book design by Anahid Hamparian

For Julia, Natalie, Amy, and Rick Sams, who were there at the beginning   —D.H.

To my good friend, Joe Hickman   —T.B.

Tinka is a fun dog,
a sun dog,
a run-and-run-and-run dog.

A joy dog,
a boy's dog,
a chews-a-brand-new-toy dog.

A sigh dog,
a cry dog,
a has-to-say-good-bye dog.

Tinka is a groan dog,
a moan dog,
a hates-to-be-alone dog.

A peek dog,

a sneak dog,

a spring-and-sprint-and-streak dog.

Tinka is a cool dog,
a school dog,

a breaking-all-the-rules dog.

A hall dog,
a ball dog,

a crash-into-the-wall dog.

A vroom dog,
a boom dog,
a messing-up-the-room dog.

Tinka is a bad dog,
a sad dog,
a makes-our-teacher-mad dog!

A "hey!" dog,
a "stay" dog,
a has-to-go-away dog.

A plead dog,
a need dog,
a come-help-us-to-read dog.

Tinka is a sweet dog,
a treat dog,
a-sitting-in-her-seat dog.

A look dog,
a nook dog,
a loves-to-hear-a-book dog.

A yay dog,
hooray dog,

a please-come-every-day dog!